# TRAFFIC JAM

## by Irma Singer
## illustrated by Peter Spacek

**Harcourt**

Orlando   Boston   Dallas   Chicago   San Diego

Visit *The Learning Site!*

**www.harcourtschool.com**

The car stops.

The bus stops.

The truck stops.

The van stops.

The fire truck
stops.

The police car
stops.

# Now the children can go!